Jesus' Life Hidden Pictures

Written by Rebecca Daniel

Illustrated by Dan Grossmann

Cover by Nancee McClure

Copyright © 1998, Shining Star
A publication of Frank Schaffer Publications

ISBN No. 0-7647-0428-1
Standardized Subject Code TA ac

Printing No. 987654321

Shining Star Publications
23740 Hawthorne Blvd.
Torrance, CA 90505

Table of Contents

To Teachers and Parents

The twenty Bible stories and hidden picture puzzles in this book will capture the heart of every young learner. The short and simple Bible-based stories give an excellent overview of the most important story ever told, the life of Jesus. Each story is followed by a challenge that reinforces the main events of the story, a hidden-picture puzzle and Scripture references so children can follow up with additional Scripture study.

Encourage the children not to mark on the hidden-picture pages so they can challenge others to find the hidden objects. The sharing of stories and hidden-picture puzzles with others will reinforce the Scripture-based learning for the child. Once the objects have been found by the children, they will take great delight in watching others search for the answers.

The puzzles and stories can be used with individuals, small groups, classes or with large groups at parties. Here are a few ways to use the stories and puzzles:

1. Give the book to individual children and let them read and complete the puzzles on their own. Small children may need assistance.
2. In the classroom setting the stories may be read to nonreaders or beginning readers, while older children can read the stories for themselves. The challenge and hidden-picture puzzle can serve as a follow-up activity.
3. Reproduce enough puzzles and stories for each member of your group and encourage each child to assemble a book of stories and hidden-picture puzzles on the life of Jesus.
4. If a time limit is given, the hidden-picture puzzles make good party games. Who can find the most hidden objects in three minutes, five minutes, etc., depending on the age of the children.
5. After hearing the story, give children an appropriate memory verse from Scripture references given at the beginning of the story. When they know the memory verses, they receive hidden pictures as awards for good work.
6. Use the puzzles in a learning center or at a learning table. Cover the hidden-picture puzzles with clear adhesive plastic. Children can use crayons to mark the answers. The answers can be rubbed off with a tissue and the puzzles can be used again by other students.

Any way you choose to use the stories and puzzles in this book, the children are sure to enjoy and learn from the experience. The highly motivating format of hidden pictures is guaranteed to provide hours of delightful learning.

SS4863

Born in a Stable

Luke 2:1-20; Matthew 1:18-25

After a long journey from Nazareth to pay taxes, Mary and Joseph found the city of Bethlehem so crowded that there was no room for them to stay in the inn. Finally the weary couple found shelter in a stable. That wondrous night Jesus was born. Mary wrapped her baby in swaddling clothes and laid Him in a manger.

There were shepherds nearby watching over their flocks. An angel of the Lord appeared to the shepherds and said, "Do not be afraid. I bring you good news of great joy that will be for all the people. Today in the town of David a Savior has been born to you; he is Christ the Lord. This will be a sign to you: You will find a baby wrapped in cloths and lying in a manger."

You can read all about the birth of Jesus in Luke 2:1-20.

Challenge

Although shepherds were the first recorded visitors to see Jesus, perhaps there were some animals in the stable that saw Him first. Looking at the picture you may think Mary and Joseph are alone with Baby Jesus. If you look closer you will find seven animals hiding in the stable. Can you see the mouse, donkey, spider, lamb, mother hen and her two baby chicks?

5

Wise Men Followed a Star
Matthew 2:1-12

When Jesus was born in Bethlehem, wise men came from the East in search of Him. These wise men followed a bright new star that they saw in the sky. They knew that the star was a sign from God that a great king had been born. They followed the star to Jerusalem and stopped at the palace of King Herod. They asked if he could direct them to the new king.

When King Herod heard that a new king had been born he was troubled. He gathered all the chief priests and scribes together and demanded that they tell him where the baby was to have been born. They looked in the Scriptures and discovered that Bethlehem was the place. He sent the wise men to Bethlehem saying, "Go and make a careful search for the child. As soon as you find him, report to me, so that I too may go and worship him."

Find out more about the wise men and the evil king's plan to destroy the new king by reading Matthew 2:1-12.

Challenge

Matthew 2:11 describes the gifts the wise men brought when they came to worship Jesus. After you read Matthew 2:11 look carefully at the picture of the wise men to see if you can find the three treasure chests that are hidden there, along with a camel and a donkey. Also hidden in the picture is Baby Jesus, the greatest gift of all.

SS4863

Jesus Visited the Temple

Luke 2:41-52

Each spring Jesus' parents attended the Feast of the Passover in Jerusalem. At this time the people thanked God for delivering their ancestors from slavery in Egypt. The year Jesus was twelve, He, went along. Jesus had many questions to ask the teachers. When His parents left to return home, Jesus stayed behind talking to the teachers in the temple.

After traveling for a day, Joseph and Mary realized that Jesus was not with them in the caravan. Frantically they returned to Jerusalem in search of their son. After a long search they found Jesus in the temple, asking questions that astonished the teachers. He showed a great deal of knowledge about God. When Mary and Joseph saw Jesus asking questions in the temple they, too, were amazed. His mother asked, "Son, why have you treated us like this? Your father and I have been anxiously searching for you."

Jesus said to them, "Why were you searching for me? Didn't you know I had to be in my Father's house?" Then Jesus went to Nazareth with His parents and was obedient to them. But His mother never forgot the things that Jesus said to her in the temple that day. You can read about this biblical adventure in Luke 2:41-52.

Challenge

Looking at the picture, it isn't difficult to spot the boy Jesus among His adult teachers. If His parents had looked in the right place, they would have found Jesus without a search. If you look in the right places, you will find hidden in the picture a scroll, Bible, lamp, candle, bell, torch, cat and mouse.

SS4863

Jesus Baptized by John

Luke 3:15-22; Matthew 3:13-17; Mark 1:9-11; John 1:29-34

Jesus lived in Nazareth with Mary and Joseph. He grew tall and strong and studied the Scriptures. When Jesus was thirty years old, his cousin, John the Baptist, was teaching and baptizing people along the Jordan River. One day as a crowd gathered at the Jordan, Jesus asked John to baptize Him. When Jesus came up out of the water, the Spirit of God descended upon Him like a dove. A voice from heaven was heard, "You are my Son, whom I love; with you I am well pleased." The crowd didn't understand or appreciate what they had witnessed. Read about John baptizing Jesus at the Jordan River in Luke 3:15-22.

Challenge

God called Jesus, "Son." There are many names for Jesus in the Bible: Christ, Messiah, Saviour, Redeemer, Word of God, Light of the World, Good Shepherd, the Great High Priest, Lamb of God, Captain of our Salvation, King of Kings, Prince of Life, Prince of Peace, the Alpha and the Omega, the Bright and Morning Star and Lion of the Tribe of Judah. Can you find symbols for some of Jesus' names hidden in the picture? Look for a candle, dove, crown, lamb, lion, star, shepherd and the Greek letters for alpha and omega.

11

The Wedding Feast

John 2:1-11

Jesus performed many miracles as He traveled about preaching and healing. He performed His first miracle at a wedding feast in Cana. The wedding was attended by His disciples, His mother and many other guests.

During the feast Jesus' mother told Him that there was no more wine to be served. Jesus told a servant to fill the water pots with water. When they were filled to the brim Jesus said, "Now draw some out and take it to the master of the banquet." When the master of the feast tasted the water, it had been turned into the finest wine.

Changing water to wine was a miracle that showed Jesus' power and convinced His disciples that He was the Son of God. Read about the first miracle performed by Jesus in John 2:1-11.

Challenge

Imagine how surprised the disciples were when they witnessed Jesus' first miracle. For the first time they began to recognize Jesus as the Messiah. As you look at the picture of the wedding feast in Cana, see if you can find the six hidden water jars that represent Jesus' first miracle. Also hidden in the picture are the wedding rings, cake and bouquet.

SS4863

Fishers of Men

Matthew 4:18-22; 9:9; 10:2-4; Luke 6:13-16

After Jesus was baptized He went into the wilderness alone for forty days to make plans for establishing God's kingdom. After rejecting every temptation put before Him by Satan, Jesus went to Bethany in search of disciples to help Him with His teaching.

While walking by the Sea of Galilee Jesus saw two brothers, Simon (Peter) and Andrew, casting a net into the sea. He said to them, "Come, follow me, and I will make you fishers of men." Simon (Peter) and Andrew left their nets and followed Jesus.

Discover how the Twelve Disciples were called by Jesus. Read Matthew 4:18-22; 9:9; 10:2-4; and Luke 6:13-16.

Challenge

Four of Jesus' disciples were fishermen—Simon (Peter), Andrew, James and John. The names of the other disciples were Philip, Bartholomew, Thomas, Matthew, James, Thaddaeus, Simon and Judas Iscariot. Look at the picture of Jesus and His four fishermen disciples. Can you find the other eight disciples hidden in the picture?

Jesus Calmed a Storm
Matthew 8:23-27; Mark 4:35-41; Luke 8:22-25

Jesus traveled with His disciples, healing and preaching. One day Jesus preached a sermon on a mountainside and described the members of God's kingdom. He said, "Blessed are the poor in spirit, for theirs is the kingdom of heaven. Blessed are those who mourn, for they will be comforted. Blessed are the meek, for they will inherit the earth. Blessed are those who hunger and thirst for righteousness, for they will be filled. Blessed are the merciful for they will be shown mercy. Blessed are the pure in heart, for they will see God. Blessed are the peacemakers, for they will be called sons of God. Blessed are those who are persecuted because of righteousness, for theirs is the kingdom of heaven." You can read the sermon Jesus gave on the mountainside in Matthew 5—7.

After the sermon Jesus asked His disciples to take Him across the Sea of Galilee. A sudden, violent storm filled the disciples with terror. When they yelled that they were going to drown, Jesus said, "You of little faith, why are you so afraid?" Then Jesus told the stormy sea to be still, and it was!

The disciples were amazed. They said, "What kind of man is this? Even the winds and the waves obey him." You can read the biblical account of the calming of the storm in Matthew 8:23-27.

Challenge

The storm undoubtedly washed supplies and parts of the boat overboard. Look at the picture of Jesus as He raised His hands to calm the storm. See if you can find some things that have washed overboard into the raging sea. If you look closely you will discover an anchor, oar, water jar, rope and one of the disciple's sandals.

SS4863

Jairus' Daughter

Matthew 9:18-19, 23-26; Mark 5:35-43; Luke 8:40-56

One day Jesus and His disciples returned to Capernaum, where a crowd had gathered to see Him. Just as Jesus began to teach, Jairus, the chief ruler of the synagogue, rushed through the crowd and fell at Jesus' feet. Jairus begged Him to come and heal his dying daughter. As Jesus, His disciples and Jairus were walking to the home of Jairus, a servant met them with the sad news that the little girl was already dead.

When Jesus reached the home, a large crowd was waiting there. Jesus said, "Go away. The girl is not dead but asleep." Some of the crowd laughed and mocked Jesus. But when He took the little girl by the hand, she got up. Since Jairus was an important man, the news about how Jesus had healed his daughter spread quickly.

Read about the miracle of Jairus' daughter being raised from the dead in Matthew 9:18-19, 23-26.

Challenge

Jairus' wife had probably nursed the little girl for many days, trying to make her happy and bring her back to health. As you study the picture of Jesus at the little girl's bedside, see if you can spot some of the things her mother thought would make her happy and healthy again. Hidden in the picture are a cup of cold water, piece of bread, chunk of cheese, bottle of medicine, vase of flowers and the little girl's doll.

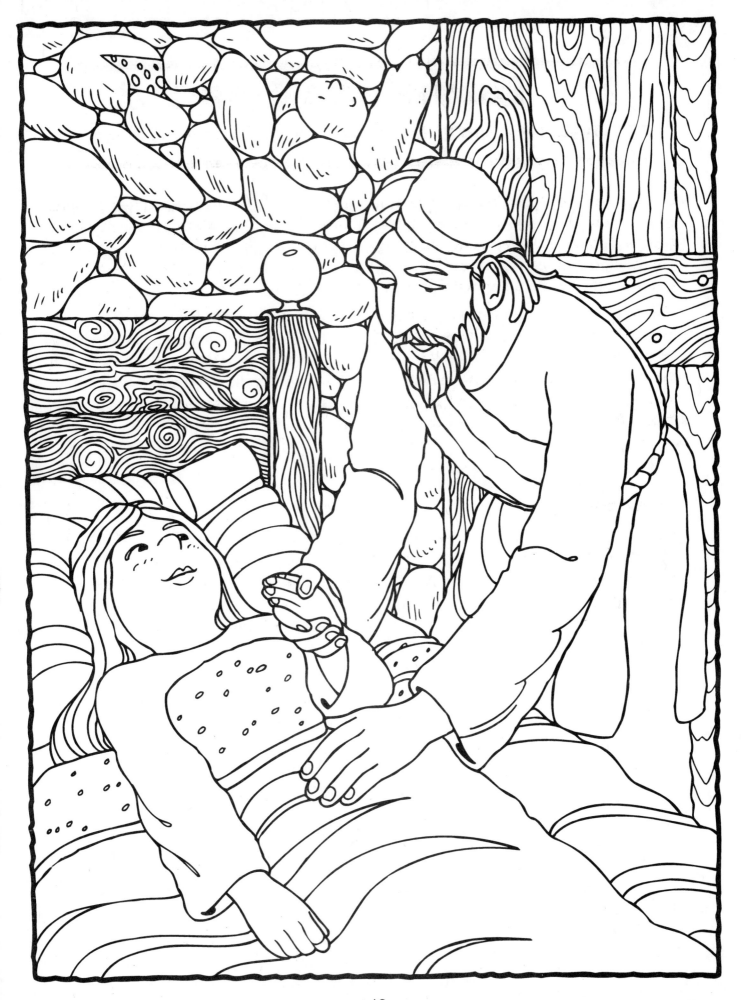

SS4863

Five Loaves and Two Fish
Matthew 14:15-21; Mark 6:30-44; Luke 9:10-17; John 6:1-13

As Jesus traveled around preaching and healing, the Pharisees watched Him angrily. Although they had no case against Jesus, they began looking for a reason to arrest Him. It was at this time that Jesus received word that His cousin, John the Baptist, had been beheaded by King Herod. Deeply saddened by the loss of John, a great prophet, Jesus and His disciples crossed the lake to go up on a mountainside to be alone.

A huge crowd gathered, wanting to hear Jesus teach. By late afternoon everyone was hungry. There was no food except a small boy's lunch of five small loaves of bread and two fish. Jesus told His disciples to pass out the food to everyone. The disciples didn't understand how such a small amount of food could feed a crowd of five thousand, but they had faith in Jesus and followed His instructions. To the amazement of all, the food fed the hungry crowd, and the leftovers filled twelve baskets.

Read the story of this miracle in Matthew 14:15-21.

Challenge

One small boy with five loaves and two fish in a crowd of five thousand wasn't much. But it was all Jesus needed to perform a great miracle. As you look at the picture of the feeding of the five thousand, see if you can find the little boy with a basket, five loaves, and two fish.

21

SS4863

Jesus Walked on Water
Matthew 14:22-33; Mark 6:45-52; John 6:15-21

After feeding five thousand people with only five loaves and two fish, Jesus dismissed the crowd and told the disciples to get in their boat and cross over to the other side of the sea. Then He went up on a mountain to pray.

That night the disciples found themselves in the middle of a raging storm. As the wind rose, the disciples cried out in terror. Suddenly they saw a figure walking on the water—it was Jesus! At first they were afraid. But Jesus said to them, "Take courage! It is I. Don't be afraid."

Peter answered Jesus, "Lord, if it's you, tell me to come to you on the water."

Jesus said, "Come." Peter left the boat and walked on the water toward Jesus. But when Peter saw the wind, he was afraid and he began to sink.

Peter cried out to Jesus, "Lord, save me." Immediately Jesus reached out His hand and caught Peter.

Jesus said to him, "You of little faith, why did you doubt?"

Read the account of this miracle in Matthew 14:22-36.

Challenge

When fear gripped them, how quickly the disciples forgot the miracles they had witnessed. But when Jesus came into the boat and the wind ceased, they worshiped Him. Do you suppose there were any sea creatures present at that miracle on the sea? Look at the picture of Jesus and Peter on the water and see if you can find the six hidden sea creatures. If you look carefully you will discover a whale, porpoise, octopus, sea horse, starfish and jellyfish.

23

Jesus Healed a Blind Man

John 9:1-12

One day as the disciples and Jesus were walking, they saw a blind man begging. The disciples asked, "Rabbi, who sinned, this man or his parents, that he was born blind?"

Jesus explained that neither the blind man nor his parents were the cause of the beggar's blindness. Jesus said, "This happened so that the work of God might be displayed in his life." Then Jesus moistened some clay, placed it over the man's eyes, and told him to go wash in the pool of Siloam. The man obeyed Jesus and was healed.

You can read the story of Jesus healing the blind man in John 9:1-12.

Challenge

How excited the begger must have been when he opened his eyes. For the first time in his life he could see! We can only imagine what objects he saw for the first time when he washed the clay from his eyes in the pool of Siloam. Perhaps he saw a dove, a rose, robin, furry spider, ladybug, caterpillar or butterfly. Can you see these objects hidden in the picture?

The Good Samaritan

Luke 10:25-37

Jesus was asked by a lawyer, "What must I do to inherit eternal life?"

Jesus answered with a question. "What is written in the law? How do you read it?"

"Love the Lord your God with all your heart and with all your soul and with all your strength and with all your mind; and, love your neighbor as yourself," replied the lawyer.

Jesus told the man a story to help him understand who his neighbor was. A traveler was going from Jerusalem to Jericho. On the way he was attacked by bandits, robbed, and left to die on the roadside. A priest came by. When he saw the dying man, he passed by on the other side of the road. A Levite (an assistant to the priest) also came and passed by.

Later a Samaritan saw the man and stopped to help him. The Good Samaritan helped the man onto his beast, took him to an inn, and cared for him. When the Good Samaritan could no longer stay with the man, he paid the innkeeper two silver coins to care for the man.

When Jesus finished the story He asked the lawyer, "Which of these three do you think was a neighbor to the man who fell into the hands of robbers?"

The lawyer replied, "The one who had mercy on him."

Jesus said, "Go and do likewise."

You can read the parable of the Good Samaritan in Luke 10:25-37.

Challenge

The Good Samaritan saved the traveler's life by carefully nursing him back to health. The Bible says the Good Samaritan poured oil and wine on the dying man's wounds, put him on his own donkey, and took him to an inn. Look at the picture of the Good Samaritan helping the man. Although the priest and the Levite were part of the story, they were not around when they were needed. Can you find them hiding in this picture? Also hidden in the picture are three thieves.

Mary and Martha
Luke 10:38-42

One day while traveling and preaching, Jesus stopped in Bethany to visit Mary and Martha, sisters of his good friend, Lazarus. Mary sat at the feet of Jesus and listened to His words. But Martha was too busy preparing food and cleaning the house to stop and listen to Jesus.

Martha became angry with her sister for not helping with the work. She complained to Jesus, "Lord, don't you care that my sister has left me to do the work by myself? Tell her to help me!"

Jesus did not tell Mary to go and help her sister. Instead He explained that the most important duty in life is to learn the will of God, as Mary had chosen to do.

Read about these two sisters in Luke 10:38-42.

Challenge

At first Martha thought her earthly duties—cooking and cleaning—were more important than listening to Jesus. But she understood when Jesus said, "Mary has chosen what is better and it will not be taken away from her." In the picture of Jesus, Mary and Martha, can you find where Martha has hidden her broom, mop, sponge, water jar, spoon, bowl and cup?

SS4863

The Lost Son
Luke 15:11-32

Jesus told many parables to the people and His disciples. One parable was about a man who had two sons. One day the younger of the sons asked his father to give him all of his inheritance so he could travel. Sadly, the father gave the boy the money and allowed him to leave.

Soon the young man had spent all his money eating and drinking and the only job he could find was caring for a farmer's pigs. The boy realized that even his father's servants lived better than he, and he decided to go home and beg forgiveness.

When the boy arrived home, his father not only forgave him but was happy to have his son back. He ordered the servants, "Quick! Bring the best robe and put it on him. Put a ring on his finger and sandals on his feet. Bring the fattened calf and kill it. Let's have a feast and celebrate. For this son of mine was dead and is alive again; he was lost and is found."

When they began the celebration, the older brother became angry and refused to go to the celebration. His father told him, "You are always with me, and everything I have is yours. But we had to celebrate and be glad because this brother of yours was dead and is alive again!"

Read this story in Luke 15:11-32.

Challenge

When the people heard Jesus telling the story of the lost son, they understood that the father in the story was really God. They understood that Jesus was telling them that God forgives us and rejoices when we come to Him. Hidden in this picture of the lost son and his father are the best robe, ring, sandals, fattened calf and two musical instruments—a flute and harp. Can you find them?

One day while at the Mount of Olives, Jesus sent two of His disciples to a village to find a colt and bring it to Him. Later that day when the disciples returned with the colt, Jesus got on it and rode into Jerusalem. Crowds of people waved palm branches and put their robes in the road to make a path for Jesus. The people had witnessed many miracles and heard about Jesus' power. They shouted praises: "Blessed is the king who comes in the name of the Lord!" and "Peace in heaven and glory in the highest!"

The angry Pharisees told Jesus to stop His disciples and followers from singing praises.

Jesus said to them, "If they keep quiet, the stones will cry out."

Read Luke 19:28-40 for the whole story.

Challenge

The Pharisees were angry because even kings on horseback and conquering heroes had never received such a welcome as the one Jesus received. Look at this picture of Jesus' triumphal entry into Jerusalem. Everyone looks joyful and happy as they sing "Hosanna!" But not everyone was happy that day. Hidden in the picture are seven very angry Pharisees. Can you find them?

 SS4863

The Money Changers

Matthew 21:12-16; Mark 11:15-18; Luke 19:45-48; John 2:13-16

News traveled quickly and by the time Jesus reached the temple in Jerusalem, many blind, lame and sick people were waiting for Him. After Jesus healed those that had gathered, the Pharisees were even more angry.

When Jesus entered the temple, He saw merchants and money changers. He began to drive out those who were buying and selling in the temple. He overturned the tables of the money changers and the benches of those that were selling doves. Jesus said that the temple should be a house of prayer, not a den of robbers.

Behind closed doors, the Pharisees and priests were plotting to arrest Jesus. Knowing that the multitudes believed Jesus was the Messiah, they devised a plan to arrest Him for treason.

You can find out more about the cleansing of the temple by reading Matthew 21:12-17.

Challenge

The money changers and merchants in the temple thought they could overcharge the people and steal. But they could not hide from Jesus. Hidden in this picture of Jesus overturning the money changers' tables are a dove, lamb, goat, ram, money bag and candlestick. Can you find the hidden objects?

35

The Lord's Supper

Matthew 26:17-29; Mark 14:12-25; Luke 22:7-23; John 13:18-30

Jesus knew that Judas had betrayed Him and had agreed to lead the Pharisees to Him for thirty pieces of silver. Jesus told Peter and John to go into Jerusalem and prepare for the Passover feast.

That evening Jesus went to the room where Peter and John had prepared the Passover meal to eat with His disciples. After Judas hurried away to meet with the Pharisees, Jesus picked up a piece of bread and gave it to His disciples. He said, "Take and eat; this is my body."

Then Jesus took the cup; gave thanks, and offered it to the disciples. He said, "Drink from it, all of you. This is my blood of the covenant, which is poured out for many for the forgiveness of sins. I tell you, I will not drink of this fruit of the vine from now on until that day when I drink it anew with you in my Father's kingdom."

You can read all about the Lord's Supper in Matthew 26:17-29.

Challenge

After the meal the disciples and Jesus sang a hymn, then went out to the Mount of Olives. Hidden in this picture are bread, a wine pitcher and twelve wine goblets. How many of the hidden objects can you find?

SS4863

In the Garden of Gethsemane

Matthew 26:36-54; Mark 14:32-46; Luke 22:39-51; John 18:1-11

After the Lord's Supper the disciples and Jesus left the upper room and went into the Garden of Gethsemane on the Mount of Olives. Jesus asked some of the disciples to wait at the entrance of the garden. He took Peter, James, and John farther into the garden.

Jesus was very sad. He asked Peter, James and John to keep watch while He prayed. But the disciples fell asleep. When Jesus returned He asked, "Could you men not keep watch with me for one hour?"

Two more times Jesus went into the garden to pray. Each time when He returned He found the disciples sleeping. The third time Jesus asked, "Are you still sleeping and resting? Look, the hour is near, and the Son of Man is betrayed into the hands of sinners. Rise, let us go! Here comes my betrayer!"

While Jesus was speaking, Judas came with a crowd of men carrying swords, sent by the chief priests and elders. They arrested Jesus and took Him away.

You can read more about Jesus in the Garden of Gethsemane in Matthew 26:36-54.

Challenge

When Judas saw that Jesus was condemned to die he took the silver back to the chief priests and elders, then went out and hanged himself. Look at this picture of Jesus praying in the garden. Can you find His three sleeping disciples, a soldier, sword and Judas with a money bag hidden in the picture?

SS4863

Jesus' Resurrection

Matthew 28:1-10; Mark 16:1-10; Luke 24:1-49; John 20:1-23

Jesus was crucified and buried on Friday. The tomb was sealed and Roman soldiers were sent by the priests and Pharisees to guard it. On the morning of the third day, the earth trembled, an angel descended and rolled back the stone in front of the tomb. The terrified soldiers fell to the ground and then ran away.

When Mary Magdalene and the other Mary reached the tomb, they found it open. An angel said, "Do not be afraid, for I know that you are looking for Jesus, who was crucified. He is not here, He has risen, just as He said. Come and see the place where he lay. Then go quickly and tell his disciples: 'He has risen from the dead and is going ahead of you into Galilee. There you will see Him.'"

As the women rushed to tell the disciples what the angel had said, Jesus met them and said, "Do not be afraid. Go and tell my brothers to go to Galilee; there they will see me."

That evening Jesus appeared to the disciples. Read Luke 24:36-48 to find out what Jesus told His disciples.

Challenge

Imagine the joy felt by the disciples and Jesus' other friends when they discovered that He was resurrected as He had said He would be. Look at the picture of the women at the tomb. Hidden in the picture are Jesus, two fleeing guards, the rock that sealed the tomb, a cross and an angel. Can you find these hidden items?

SS4863

Jesus' Ascension into Heaven

John 21:1-14; Matthew 28:16-20; Mark 16:14-20; Luke 24:36-51

Jesus appeared to His disciples a number of times after His resurrection. One day at the Sea of Tiberias while some of His disciples were fishing, Jesus stood on the shore. The disciples didn't recognize Him. Jesus called out to them, "Friends, haven't you any fish?"

The disciples had not caught any fish all day and they answered, "No." Jesus told them to cast their nets on the right side of their boat. They obeyed and suddenly the net was so full the men could hardly pull it into the boat. Then the disciples knew that the stranger on the shore was Jesus.

Forty days after Jesus' resurrection He took His disciples to the Mount of Olives. While He blessed them, He ascended into heaven.

The disciple John wrote, "Jesus did many other things as well. If every one of them were written down, I suppose that even the whole world would not have room for the books that would be written."

To learn more about the forty days between Jesus' resurrection and His ascension, study the Bible verses listed above.

Challenge

"They were looking intently up into the sky as he was going, when suddenly two men dressed in white stood beside them. 'Men of Galilee,' they said, 'Why do you stand here looking into the sky? This same Jesus, who has been taken from you into heaven, will come back in the same way you have seen him go into heaven.'" (Acts 1:10-11)

Hidden in this picture of Jesus' ascension are symbols that remind us that Jesus will return. Can you find the loaf of bread, throne, crown, dove, lamb and Bible?

Answer Key

Page 5

Page 7

Page 9

Page 11

Page 13

Page 15

Page 17

Page 19

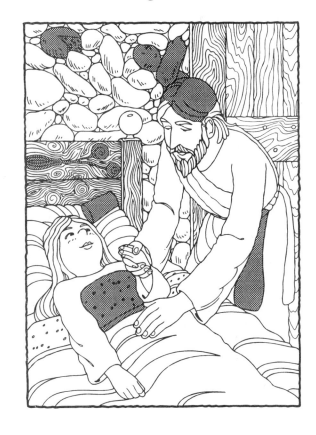

SS4863

Page 21

Page 23

Page 25

Page 27

SS4863

Page 29

Page 31

Page 33

Page 35

Page 37

Page 39

Page 41

Page 43

SS4863